ROCK
& POP

ROCK & POP

TRINITY
COLLEGE LONDON

THE EXAM AT A GLANCE

For your Rock & Pop exam you will need to perform a set of **three songs** and one of the **Session skills** assessments, either **Playback** or **Improvising**. You can choose the order in which you play your set-list.

Song 1

Choose a song from this book

OR from www.trinityrock.com

Song 2

Choose a different song from this book

OR from www.trinityrock.com

OR perform a song you have chosen yourself: this could be your own cover version or a song you have written. It should be at the same level as the songs in this book. See the website for detailed requirements.

Song 3: Technical focus

Choose one of the Technical focus songs from this book, which cover three specific technical elements.

Session skills

Choose either **Playback** or **Improvising**.

When you are preparing for your exam please check on **www.trinityrock.com** for the most up-to-date information and requirements as these can change from time to time.

CONTENTS

Tuning track: E, A, D, G with a pause between each note.

Trinity College London's Rock & Pop syllabus and supporting publications have been devised and produced in association with Faber Music and Peters Edition London.

Trinity College London
Registered office:
89 Albert Embankment
London SE1 7TP UK
T + 44 (0)20 7820 6100
F + 44 (0)20 7820 6161
E music@trinitycollege.co.uk
www.trinitycollege.co.uk

Registered in the UK. Company no. 02683033
Charity no. 1014792
Patron HRH The Duke of Kent KG

Copyright © 2012 Trinity College London
First published in 2012 by Trinity College London

Second impression, October 2012

Cover and book design by Chloë Alexander
Brand development by Andy Ashburner @ Caffeinehit (www.caffeinehit.com)
Photographs courtesy of Rex Features Limited.
Printed in England by Caligraving Ltd

Audio produced, mixed and mastered by Tom Fleming
Bass arranged by Tom Fleming
Backing tracks arranged by Tom Fleming
Musicians
Vocals: Bo Walton, Brendan Reilly & Alison Symons
Keyboards: Oliver Weeks
Guitar & Bass: Tom Fleming
Bass: Ben Hillyard
Drums: George Double
Studio Engineer: Joel Davies www.thelimehouse.com

ISBN: 978-0-85736-229-2

SONGS YOU REALLY GOT ME

The Kinks
Words and Music by Ray Davies

♩ = 138 **Rock** *2 bars count-in*

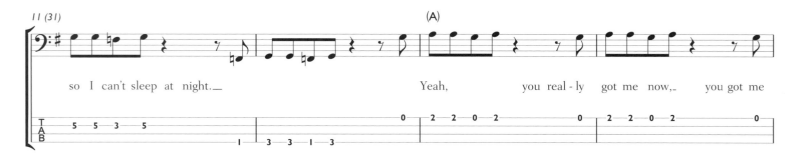

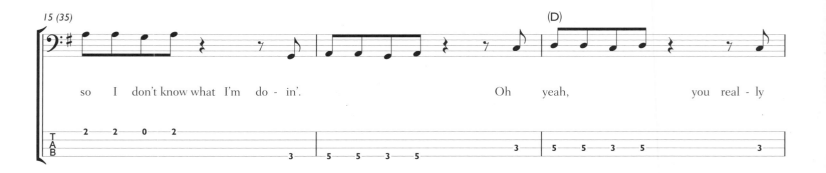

so   I   don't know what I'm   do - in'.   Oh   yeah,   you real - ly

Chorus

got me go - in',   you got me   so I can't sleep at night. You   real - ly got me,   you

1.

real - ly got me,   you real - ly   got me.

2.

Outro

real - ly   got me.

SONGS NEED YOU TONIGHT

INXS
Words and Music by Andrew Farriss and Michael Hutchence

♩ = 108 **Rock** *2 bars count-in*

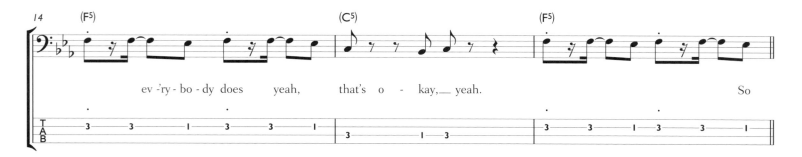

Chorus I

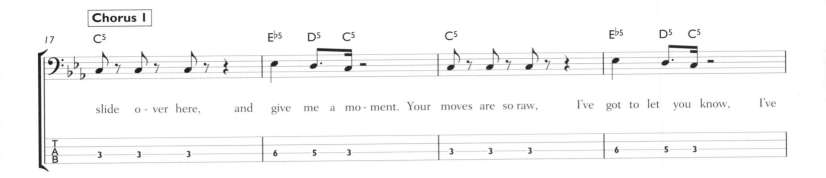

slide o-ver here, and give me a mo-ment. Your moves are so raw, I've got to let you know, I've

got to let you know: you're one of my kind.___

Verse 2

I need you to-night,___

'cause I'm not sleep-ing, there's some-thing a-bout

___ you girl,___ that makes me sweat.

www.trinityrock.com

BASS GRADE 2   7

So how do you feel? I'm lone - ly._____ What do you think? Can't

think at all.__ What you gonna do? Gonna live my life.__ So

Chorus 2

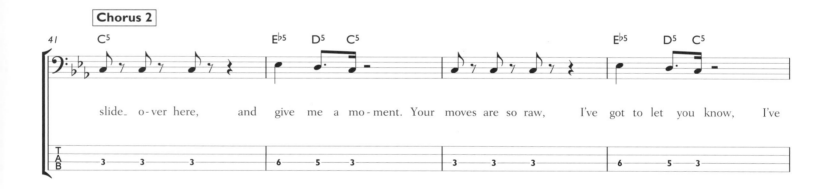

slide_ o - ver here, and give me a mo - ment. Your moves are so raw, I've got to let you know, I've

got to let you know: you're one of my__ kind.__

SONGS SPIRIT IN THE SKY

Norman Greenbaum
Words and Music by Norman Greenbaum

♩ = 120 **Swung** *2 bars count-in*

Lyrics:

1. When I die and they lay me to rest,— gon-na go___ to the place___ that's the best,
2. Go-in' up to the spirit in the sky,— that's where I'm gonna go when I die,

when I lay me down___ to die,— gon-na go___ to the spi-rit___ in the sky.___
when I die and they lay me to rest, gon-na go___ to the place that's the best.

SONGS COMFORTABLY NUMB

Pink Floyd
Words and Music by Roger Waters and David Gilmour

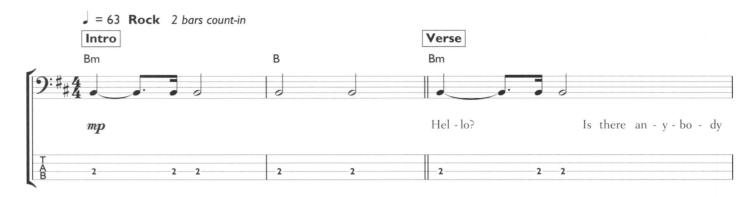

Chorus

mf There is no pain__ you are__ re - ced - ing, a dis - tant ship's smoke on the hor-

- i - zon. You are on - ly com - ing through in waves,__ your

lips move__ but I can't hear__ what you're say - ing.

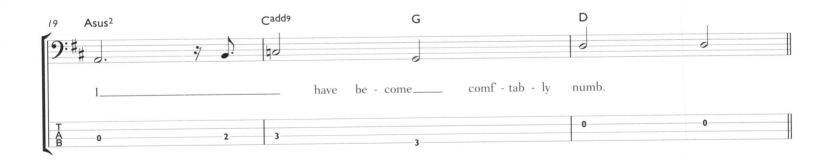

I_____ have be - come__ comf - tab - ly numb.

Outro

YOUR PAGE NOTES

ROCK AROUND THE CLOCK

In your exam, you will be assessed on the following technical elements:

1 Counting

In the intro, the bass part starts with a series of stabs that are cued by the vocals, and should be exactly in time with the drums. Listen to the vocals and count carefully to make sure that you play the stabs accurately.

You will need to count the three beats' rest in bar 47 to make sure that you come in exactly at the beginning of the following bar.

2 Boogie-woogie bass line

The verse of 'Rock Around The Clock' features a boogie-woogie bass line. Your steady ♩ beat lays a firm foundation for the song, so it is important that you keep strictly in time with the drums. Aim for a full rounded tone.

Watch out for the accidental (F♮) in bars 12 and 36.

3 Balance

During the guitar solo (bars 33–40), make sure that the bass part is balanced against the guitar. Allow the soloist to be heard.

When the bass takes over the solo at bar 41, make sure that you play like a soloist – loud enough to be heard over the band. Enjoy the chance to take the lead for a few bars.

ROCK AROUND THE CLOCK

TRACK **10** demo TRACK **11** backing

Bill Haley and his Comets
Words and Music by Max C. Freedman and Jimmy De Knight

♩ = 140 **Swing shuffle** *2 bars count-in*

One, two, three o'clock, four o'clock, rock. Five, six, se-ven o'clock, eight o'clock, rock.

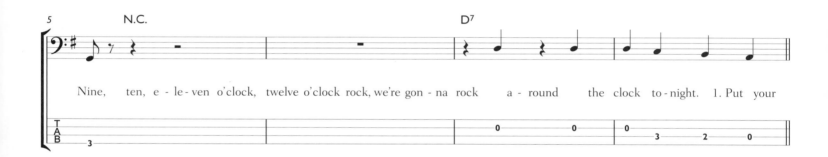

Nine, ten, e-le-ven o'clock, twelve o'clock rock, we're gon-na rock a-round the clock to-night. 1. Put your

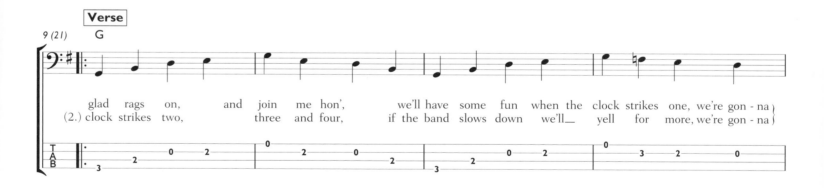

glad rags on, and join me hon', we'll have some fun when the clock strikes one, we're gon-na
(2.) clock strikes two, three and four, if the band slows down we'll yell for more, we're gon-na

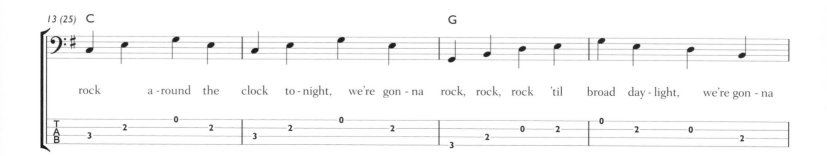

rock a-round the clock to-night, we're gon-na rock, rock, rock 'til broad day-light, we're gon-na

rock, gon-na rock a - round_ the clock to - night.___

2. When the

Guitar solo

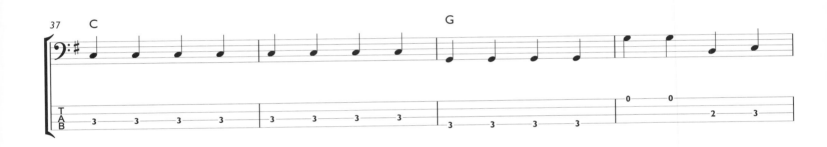

Bass solo

Outro

MEAN JUMPER BLUES

In your exam, you will be assessed on the following technical elements:

1 Playing a riff

A riff is a phrase that is repeated many times throughout a song. This minor blues song is built around a bass riff using the chords Am and Dm. Make sure that you observe the rests and do not allow notes to ring during the rests. This will help to create a really dirty, bluesy feel and should contrast with the ♩ on the last beat of each bar, which should be held on for the full value.

2 Playing fills

At various points (bar 8, for example), the bass breaks out of the riff to play short fills that lead into a chord change. Look out for these fills and use them to add interest to the performance. You could play them a little louder than the riff, and you could shape them so that they lead into the new chord.

3 Dynamics

There are several changes of dynamic towards the end of the bridge section. Keep the volume down a little at the beginning of this section – this will allow you to make a really dramatic *crescendo* up to *f* at the end of this section. Play each note louder than the one before and end with a strong accent (>) on the last note. Then drop straight down to *mp* for the outro.

TECHNICAL FOCUS SONGS

MEAN JUMPER BLUES

Blind Lemon Jefferson
Words and Music by Blind Lemon Jefferson

♩ = 90 **Blues** *2 bars count-in*

Verses

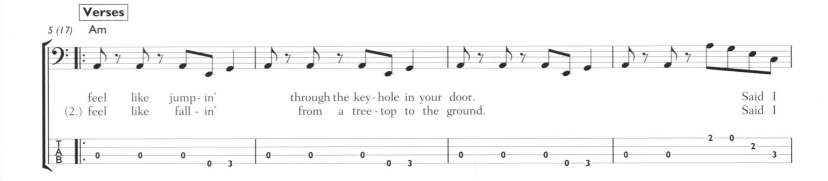

feel   like   jump-in'   through the key-hole in your door.   Said I
(2.) feel like   fall-in'   from   a tree-top to the ground.   Said I

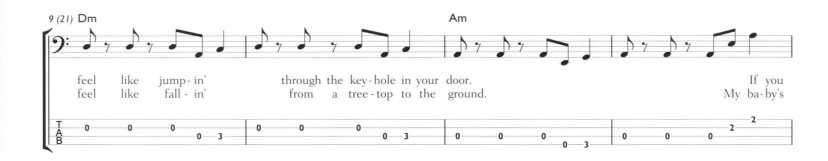

feel   like   jump-in'   through the key-hole in your door.   If you
feel   like   fall-in'   from   a tree-top to the ground.   My ba-by's

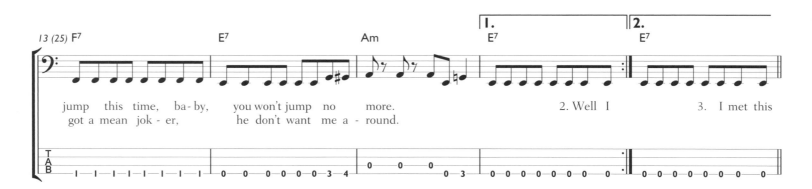

jump   this time, ba-by,   you won't jump no   more.   2. Well I   3. I met this
got a mean jok-er,   he don't want me a-round.

YOU REALLY GOT ME

The Kinks

The Kinks were one of the most influential bands of the 1960s. A four-piece London Mod band, they produced short punchy songs, often with high-quality lyrics written by their singer Ray Davies. Like many British bands of the time, they began as an R&B group but, over their long career, their style changed more than once. They had a string of hit singles during the 1960s, including 'You Really Got Me' (1964), which reached No. 1.

This raw energetic song with its angry guitar riffs, power chords and minimalist lyrics is often described as both the first heavy metal hit and the first punk hit.

This song has one of the best-known rock riffs of all time. It needs to be energetic but also rhythmically tight. Listen to the guitar, which also plays the riff, and make sure that you are playing exactly together.

Come off the last note of each repetition of the riff cleanly, so that the rests between them are well defined.

Dynamics are important – leave some room to get louder in the choruses.

The bass breaks out of the riff twice in the song:
- at bar 23, the C needs to be played firmly and ring almost to the end of the next bar
- the outro uses syncopation before ending with a held note.

Listen carefully to the backing track and finish the song cleanly and exactly at the same time as the backing.

'*I* always *wanna* be. *by* your *side*'

NEED YOU TONIGHT

INXS

'Need You Tonight' comes from the album *Kick* (1987) by the Australian band INXS. The band was made up of three Farriss brothers, fronted by the charismatic singer Michael Hutchence. Their catchy music could be described as slick, danceable rock, laden with riffs and hooks.

The signature riff of this song suddenly appeared in the head of the songwriter Andrew Farriss just as he was getting into a taxi. He asked the taxi driver to wait for a minute while he picked up something from his motel room: he reappeared much later having made a quick recording of the riff.

'Need You Tonight' uses two riffs – one in the verses and another in the choruses. Get both grooving nicely and you will be on your way to a great performance.

Articulation is very important in this song – the gaps between the notes are as important as the notes themselves. Make sure that you:
- give plenty of room to the rests
- keep all the *staccato* (detached) notes short
- contrast the detached playing (in, for example, bar 3) with the smoother passages (in, for example, bar 4).

'So *slide* over *here*, and *give* me a *moment*'

SPIRIT IN THE SKY

Norman Greenbaum

'Spirit In The Sky' was both a worldwide hit and a one-hit-wonder for Norman Greenbaum in 1969. Taken from the album of the same name, the song is an interesting mix of gospel-inspired lyrics and psychedelic rock, with much use of heavily distorted electric guitar. The guitar techniques and effects were very experimental for the time. The characteristic guitar sound was produced using a Fender Telecaster with a fuzz box built into the body.

The song has been used in many advertisements, films and television shows. Several cover versions have been made, the two most successful by Doctor and the Medics (1986) and Gareth Gates (2003) – both of these were No. 1 in the UK charts.

In the intro and chorus of 'Spirit In The Sky', the role of the bass is to lay down a firm foundation for the rhythm and the harmony. Do not underestimate the bass part – it may look easy, but the feel and dynamics make a real difference to the song. Listen to the backing track and play it in a way that complements the rest of the band.

The Ds in this song are sometimes played on the fifth fret of the A string and sometimes on the open D string.

In the outro you need to:
- use muting to make the rests clean
- put accents on the notes D and C
- watch out for the syncopation in the 'pushes' at the ends of bars 29, 31 and 33.

'Gonna *go* to *the* place *that's* the *best*'

COMFORTABLY NUMB

Pink Floyd

'Comfortably Numb' comes from Pink Floyd's 1980 album *The Wall.* Pink Floyd was founded in 1966 by bassist Roger Waters and singer-guitarist Syd Barrett. The band combined lush production with extensive sound effects and an eclectic musical style embracing blues, jazz rock and psychedelia, all helping to create a dark atmospheric world.

Pink Floyd became well-known for their spectacular live performances, playing outdoors to massive audiences. For live performances of *The Wall*, roadies constructed a huge wall across the stage which was dramatically demolished to reveal the band. *The Wall* was later made into an ambitious film directed by Alan Parker.

This song should be grandiose and atmospheric. Aim to create this mood in your playing.

A slow song like 'Comfortably Numb' does not require great agility to play, but it still has challenges. At slow speeds, tone becomes very important, so focus on making the sound of each note full and round.

At slower speeds, articulation can also be heard very clearly. Keep the *staccato* notes in bars 4, 6, 8 and 10 short and detached. But, in the same bars make sure that you hold the long notes on for their full length so they flow smoothly into the next notes.

Watch out for the ♪. notes at the end of bars 14, 16 and 19. These should be well-placed, so that they add a sense of momentum: they are important moments in this song.

'Is *there* anyone *home?*'

ROCK AROUND THE CLOCK

Bill Haley And His Comets

This Bill Haley And His Comets song was, for many people, the first rock 'n' roll music that they heard. It is hard to imagine the far-reaching and powerful effect that it had on its audience.

The use of 'Rock Around The Clock' on the soundtrack of the 1955 film *Blackboard Jungle* helped to cement the association of rock 'n' roll with teenage rebellion and when, a year later, the film *Rock Around The Clock* was released in cinemas across the United States and Europe, it caused a sensation. Audiences were dancing in the aisles and out on the streets and there were unruly, sometimes violent scenes. In some places the film was banned and rock 'n' roll was denounced from the pulpit.

The raw and punchy song became a symbol of the teenage generation and soon sold millions of copies.

PERFORMANCE · HINTS & TIPS

'Rock Around The Clock' should finish with a confident outro. Watch out for:
- the accidental (C♯) in bar 46
- the *staccato* note in bar 47.

Make sure that you hit the last note of the song exactly in time to give the piece a really strong finish. This note has an accent (>): make it louder than the other notes.

'We'll have some fun when the clock strikes one'

MEAN JUMPER BLUES

Blind Lemon Jefferson

'Mean Jumper Blues' is a 12-bar blues first recorded by the Texan blues singer and guitarist Blind Lemon Jefferson. Like most blues (early American black music originally performed by one singer accompanied on guitar or banjo), 'Mean Jumper Blues' has four beats in a bar and is built around a three-line verse, where the second line is a repeat of the first.

As a young man, Blind Lemon Jefferson was a poverty-stricken wandering street musician. Despite this, he built up a good reputation and, in 1925, became one of the first country blues musicians to get a recording contract. These early recordings went on to have a big influence on rock musicians. Many artists have covered his songs, including Bob Dylan, Grateful Dead and Counting Crows. Blind Lemon Jefferson froze to death in 1929 during a snow storm, having had a heart attack.

This song does not start on the first beat of the bar but on the final ♪ – this is usually known as a 'pick up' (or sometimes called an upbeat or *anacrusis*). But the bass riff starts on the first beat of the bar, after the pick-up note played by the guitar. Be sure to come in at the right place.

The song is marked **mf** at the start and stays that way right through to bar 34, where there is a *crescendo* (◁———◁). You then drop right down to **mp** (*mezzo piano*) for the outro. Make sure these dynamics are clearly contrasted.

This song is also in the vocals, guitar, keyboards and drums books, so you can get together and play it in a band.

'*If you* jump *this* time, *baby,* you *won't* jump *no* more'

PLAYBACK

For your exam, you can choose either Playback or Improvising (see page 28).
If you choose Playback, you will be asked to play some music you have not seen
or heard before.

In the exam, you will be given the song chart and the examiner will play a recording
of the music. You will hear several two-bar phrases on the recording: you should play
each of them straight back in turn. There's a rhythm track going throughout, which
helps you keep in time. There should not be any gaps in the music.

In the exam you will have two chances to play with the recording:
- First time – for practice
- Second time – for assessment.

You should listen to the audio, copying what you hear; you can also read the music.
Here are some practice song charts which are also on the CD in this book.

Don't forget that the Playback test can include requirements which may not be
shown in these examples, including those from earlier grades. Check the parameters
at www.trinityrock.com to prepare for everything which might come up in your exam.

'I really *like* the *way* music *looks* on *paper.* It *looks* like *art* to *me*'

Steve Vai

Practice playback 1

Practice playback 2

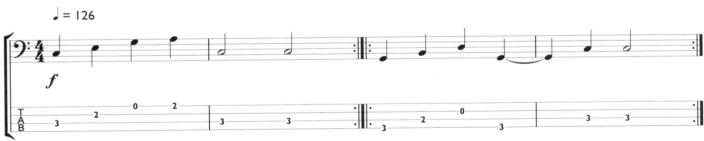

IMPROVISING

For your exam, you can choose either Playback (see page 26), or Improvising. If you choose to improvise, you will be asked to improvise over a backing track that you haven't heard before in a specified style.

In the exam, you will be given a song chart and the examiner will play a recording of the backing track. The backing track consists of a passage of music played on a loop. You should improvise a bass line which fits the track.

In the exam you will have two chances to play with the recording:
- First time – for practice
- Second time – for assessment.

Here are some improvising charts for practice which are also on the CD in this book.

Don't forget that the Improvising test can include requirements which may not be shown in these examples, including those from earlier grades. Check the parameters at www.trinityrock.com to prepare for everything which might come up in your exam.

Practice improvisation 1

♩ = 110 **Heavy Rock**

| D | G | A | Em |

Practice improvisation 2

♩ = 100 **Country**

| F | Dm | C | G |

CHOOSING A SONG FOR YOUR EXAM

There are lots of options to help you choose your three songs for the exam. For Songs 1 and 2, you can choose a song which is:

*   from this book
*   from www.trinityrock.com

Or for Song 2 you can choose a song which is:

*   sheet music from a printed or online source
*   your own arrangement of a song or a song you have written yourself (see page 30).

You can play the song unaccompanied or with a backing track (minus the bass part). If you like, you can create a backing track yourself (or with friends), or you could add your own vocals – or both.

For Grade 2, the song should last between one and three-and-a-half minutes, and the level of difficulty should be similar to your other songs. When choosing a song, think about:

*   Does it work on my instrument?
*   Are there any technical elements that are too difficult for me? (If so, perhaps save it for when you do the next grade.)
*   Do I enjoy playing it?
*   Does it work with my other pieces to create a good set-list?

See www.trinityrock.com for further information and advice on choosing your own song.

SHEET MUSIC

You must always bring an original copy of the book or a download sheet with email certificate for each song you perform in the exam. If you choose to write your own song you must provide the examiner with a copy of the sheet music. Your music can be:

*   a lead sheet with lyrics, chords and melody line
*   a chord chart with lyrics
*   a full score using conventional staff/TAB notation
*   see page 30 for details on presenting a song you have written yourself.

The title of the song and your name should be on the sheet music.

HELP PAGES

WRITING YOUR OWN SONG

You can play a song that you have written yourself for one of the choices in your exam. For Grade 2, your song should last between one and three-and-a-half minutes, so it is likely to be quite straightforward. It is sometimes difficult to know where to begin, however. Here are some suggestions for starting points:

- **A melody**: many songs are made up around a 'hook' (a short catchy melodic idea, usually only a few notes long).
Try writing a couple of ideas for hooks here:

- **A riff**: a riff is a very short melodic or rhythmic idea which is repeated over and over. It often underpins an entire song. Write a couple of short riffs here:

WRITING YOUR SONG DOWN

Rock and pop music is often written as a **lead sheet** with the lyrics (if there are any), chords and a melody line.

- As a bass player, you may want to write your part on a **five-line stave** or as **tab**. Both have been used for the songs in this book.

- You can, if you prefer, use a **graph** or **table** to represent your music, as long as it is clear to anyone else (including the examiner) how the song goes.

- **A word or phrase, theme or subject**: certain words and subjects suggest particular styles of music: a song about riding a motorbike might have a driving rhythm, a love song could be more reflective.

There are plenty of other ways of starting: perhaps with a chord sequence or a lyric, for example.

You will also need to consider the **structure** of your song (verse and chorus, 12-bar blues, and so on), the **style** it is in (blues, hard rock, etc.), and what **instruments** it is for (e.g. voice/keyboards/bass/drums . . .).

There are many choices to be made – which is why writing a song is such a rewarding thing to do.

PLAYING IN A BAND

Playing in a band is exciting: it can be a lot of fun and, as with everything, the more you do it, the easier it gets. It is very different from playing on your own. Everyone contributes to the overall sound: the most important skill you need to develop is listening.

For a band to sound good, the players need to be 'together' – that mainly means keeping in time with each other, but also playing at the same volume, and with the same kind of feeling.

Your relationship with the other band members is also important. Talk with them about the music you play, the music you like, and what you'd like the band to achieve short-term and long-term.

Band rehearsals are important – you should not be late, tired or distracted by your mobile phone! Being positive makes a huge difference. Try to create a friendly atmosphere in rehearsals so that everybody feels comfortable trying out new things. Don't worry about making mistakes: that is what rehearsals are for.

'Mean Jumper Blues' (page 18) is arranged for band. You will find parts for vocals, guitar, keyboard and drums in the other Trinity Rock & Pop Grade 2 books or available online. There are also parts for 'Rock Around The Clock' in Trinity Rock & Pop Grade 2 Guitar and Drums books. Trinity offers exams for groups of musicians at various levels. The songs arranged for bands are ideal to include as part of a set-list for these exams. Have a look at the website for more details.

HINTS AND TIPS

- Your own ability as a musician is important – if you have practised different techniques on your own, then you will have more to offer to the band. It is worth remembering that simple parts can be very effective, it is not always necessary for each instrument to play every note in the chord, or on every beat of the bar.

- Listen to how your part fits with the rest of the band. Each instrument should contribute something different to the overall sound: having different instruments play similar parts rarely sounds good.

- Some instruments could stop playing in certain sections. This is a very effective way of increasing the range of dynamics.

PLAYING WITH BACKING TRACKS

The CD contains demos and backing tracks of all the songs in the book. The additional songs at www.trinityrock.com also come with demos and backing tracks.

- In your exam, you should perform with the backing track, or you can create your own (see below).
- The backing tracks begin with a click track, which sets the tempo and helps you start accurately.
- Be careful to set the balance between the volume of the backing track and your instrument.
- Listen carefully to the backing track to ensure you are playing in time.

If you are creating your own backing track here are some further tips:
- Make sure the sound quality is of a good standard.
- Think carefully about the instruments/sounds you are putting on the backing track.
- Avoid copying what you are playing on the backing track – it should support not duplicate.
- Do you need to include a click track at the beginning?

COPYRIGHT IN A SONG

If you are a singer or songwriter it is important to know about copyright. When someone writes a song or creates an arrangement they own the copyright (sometimes called 'the rights') to that version. The copyright means that other people cannot copy it, sell it, perform it in a concert, make it available online or record it without the owner's permission or the appropriate licence. When you write a song you automatically own the copyright to it, which means that other people cannot copy your work. But just as importantly, you cannot copy other people's work, or perform it in public without their permission or the appropriate licence.

Points to remember
- You can create a cover version of a song for an exam or other non-public performance.
- You cannot record your cover version and make your recording available to others (by copying it or uploading it to a website) without the appropriate licence.
- You own the copyright of your own original song, which means that no one is allowed to copy it.
- You cannot copy someone else's song without their permission or the appropriate licence.
- If you would like to use somebody else's words in your own song you must check if they are in copyright and, if so, we recommend you confirm with the author that they are happy for the words to be used as lyrics.
- Materials protected by copyright can normally be used as lyrics in our examinations as these are private performances under copyright law. The examiner may ask you the name of the original author in the exam.
- When you present your own song to the examiner, make sure you include the title, the names of any writers and the source of your lyrics.